WiLDCAT
KEEPS GOING

Cartoons by Donald Rooum. Colour by Jayne Clementson. Published by Freedom Press.

Wildcat keeps going

Cartoons by Donald Rooum
Coloured by Jayne Clementson

First published 2011

Freedom Press
(in Angel Alley)
84b Whitechapel High Street
London E1 7QX

ISBN 978-1-904491-14-9

Printed in Great Britain by
Aldgate Press, London E1

THE REBUS
A REBUS IS A
VISUAL PUN.
IN 1980,
BRITAIN'S CHIEF
LAW OFFICER WAS
QUINTIN <u>HOGG</u>.

MR BLOCK
DEVISED BY
ERNEST RIEBE.
FIRST PUBLISHED
1912 IN THE
INDUSTRIAL WORKER

KEWPIE
DOLL

MYSTERY

REVOLTING
PUSSYCAT

FREERANGE
EGGHEAD

WILDCAT

Jean Charles de Menezes was the victim of a tragic accident. He was mistakenly identified as a suicide bomber.

Ian Tomlinson was another unfortunate accident victim. He was mistaken for a cheeky peaceful demonstrator.

So what about ...??

Blair Peach ?? No accident there. He really was a cheeky peaceful demonstrator.

People feel safe when they see police on the streets.

Be on the safe side. Make no comment.

8

9

WILDCAT

Yes, Pussycat, we're all working for a classless society,

but as the first step, the working class must take power.

Right. What keeps the powerful in power is the acquiescence of ordinary people.

Glad you agree. Ordinary people must acquiesce in the workers being the bosses for a change.

The way I mean it, workers and ordinary people are the same.

Who are "the workers" you say ordinary people must accept as bosses?

TICK TOCK TICK TOCK

OK, myself and a few comrades. But

WE KNOW WHAT THE WORKERS NEED.

What the British did to prisoners during the Mau Mau business in Kenya in 1953 – It couldn't happen today.

PAPERS REVEAL BRUTAL TREATMENT

That's what they were saying in 1953, about the British atrocities in South Africa during the Boer War in 1901.

And in another fifty years it's what they'll be saying about what the British did in Afghanistan.

(unless, of course, either the anarchist revolution has happened or the human species has gone extinct)

15

19

20

24

WILDCAT

VOTE FOR NOBODY.

Because i want NOBODY to be in power.

But there's no chance of nobody in power.

So?? There's no chance of yogic flyers in power, but people who **want** them in power vote for them.

i want nobody in power, so i vote for NOBODY.

Hoho!! Very witty!! But...

you can't elect perfection. You can only vote for the least worse alternative.

Not voting is voting for the Tories!!

HEATED ARGUMENT

DETAIL OF DRAWING BY HUNT EMERSON. THANKS.

As i thought !!! Not voting is voting for nobody.

26

WILDCAT

Anarchy!! Everyone doing whatever they like, but not impairing anyone else's freedom. A nice idea, but not really possible, is it??

Opinions differ. But anarchism isn't about dreams of perfection in some distant future. Charlotte Wilson, the anarchist who started *Freedom* in 1886, said the purpose of society is to give every individual the **largest possible opportunities in life.**

And since 1886, have opportunities in life increased as a result of anarchist agitation??

giggle

Not a lot, but perhaps a bit. In Britain, in my lifetime, a lot of harmless sexual acts have been decriminalised.

Gaaargh!!! "harmless sexual acts!!!"

You say you're for <u>freedom</u>. But what you're advocating: **permissiveness!!!**

You see, Pussycat, some people who say anarchy is a nice idea are in fact **against** freedom.

STAMP!! STAMP!! STAMP!!

What's up with you?

All this woffle!! I think cartoons should be funny.

Roobm

29

31

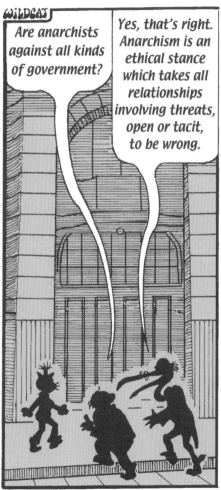

YOU have chosen your local council.

Don't blame ME, mate. I didn't vote.

Those who didn't vote don't have a say in local decisions.

Nor have those who voted for defeated candidates.

...Nor even those who voted for successful candidates.

Once elected, the councillors make all the decisions.

Oh, if only that were true!!

A COUNCILLOR

Most local decisions are made in Westminster, and/or by bureaucrats...

But voting gives your local councillor a bit of encouragement.

That's what local democracy is all about.

41

44

The Wildcat comic strip was begun
in a paper called *Wildcat* in 1975.
It moved to *Freedom* in January 1980,
and has since appeared in every issue.
There are seven collections in print.

Wildcat anarchist comics
Introduction by Philip Sansom
ISBN 0 900384 30 1 (1985 reprinted 1987 1995 2004)

Wildcat strikes again
ISBN 0 900384 47 6 (1989 reprinted 1999)

Wildcat ABC of bosses
Foreword by Tony Gibson
ISBN 0 900384 60 3 (1991 reprinted 2004 2009)

Health Service Wildcat
Scripts by Victoria N. Furmurry
ISBN 0 900384 73 5 (1994)

Twenty year millenium Wildcat
ISBN 0 900384 97 2 (1999)

Wildcat anarchists against bombs
ISBN 1 904491 01 4 (2003)

Wildcat keeps going
Coloured by Jayne Clementson
ISBN 978 1 904491 14 9 (2011)

Anarchists against copyright!!